W9-ALX-214

Consultant on this book—
Dr. Paul Witty, Director
Psycho-Educational Clinic
Northwestern University

The "I Want to Be" books are designed to encourage independent reading on beginner level. The concept—broad as a child's imagination—brings pleasure to early reading experience and better understanding of the world. But the text is in line with the young reader's skill.

All but thirteen of the one-hundred-eighty-seven words of the vocabulary used in this book are from *The First Thousand Words for Children's Reading.*

FOLK TALES
Horse Stories
HISTORY
SCIENCE

I want to be a

LIBRARIAN

By Carla Greene
Illustrations by Frances Eckart

CHILDRENS PRESS, CHICAGO

Library of Congress Catalog Card Number: 60-6674

Copyright, 1960, Childrens Press
Printed in the U.S.A.

Jane walked
toward the library.

She had never been
inside the library.

"I wish Joe had come
with me," she thought.

Joe was Jane's
big brother. He would
not come to the library.
He had a fine new boat.

Jane went up to the door of the library.

She read what it said on the door.

STORY HOUR

9-10

Then she opened the door and went in.

STORY HOUR
9-10

"What a nice room,"
thought Jane.

There were books and
pictures everywhere.

Boys and girls
sat in a half-circle.

Miss Brown was the
librarian.

She smiled at Jane.

"Come and sit here,"
she said.

3 PIGS

MICE
3 PIGS
ALICE

Miss Brown told a story that Jane liked.

It was about a boy who had many animal friends.

"I want to read all the animal books in the library," said Jane.

Miss Brown smiled. "That will take you a long time. There are many animal books here."

"May I have a library card of my own?" asked Jane.

"Yes," said Miss Brown. "Write your name here and take this card to your mother. Bring it back next week. Then I will give you your card."

"Thank you, Miss Brown,"

said Jane.

The next week
Jane got her library
card. But which books
should she choose?

There were books about
pigs and kittens
and bears and kings
and goats and ducks
and other things.

"I like dog stories,"
said Jane.

Miss Brown showed Jane
some drawers full of cards.

"Let's look at the
cards with the word DOG
at the top. These cards
have the names of books
about dogs. See the
number on each card. That
tells me where to find
the book."

Miss Brown found two books about dogs. They were books that Jane could read.

"And I would like this book, too," said Jane. It was called, HOW TO SAIL A BOAT.

"That book is hard to read," said Miss Brown.

"My brother, Joe, will like this," said Jane.

DOGS

Miss Brown put a date on a card in each book.

"Bring the books back on this date," she said. "Don't be late. You must pay a fine for late books."

"I will take good care of the books and bring them back on time," said Jane.

E

"This is a wonderful book," said Joe. "It tells me what I want to know about sailing. I want to be a good sailor. What do you want to be, Jane?"

"I want to be a good librarian, someday," said Jane. "I will help people find good books."

"Miss Brown does other things, too," said Joe.

She chooses the best books for the children's room.

She mends books that are worn with use.

She helps
teachers
find books
and pictures
and songs.

She puts new
books on the
shelves. And she
puts cards for
them in the
drawers.

"How do you get to be a librarian, Miss Brown?" asked Jane.

"You should go through college, Jane," said Miss Brown. "Then you should study another year in a Library School. And you should like children and books."

797.1 BOATING

One day Miss Brown let Jane help her.

They drove out into the country.

"Here comes the book bus!" cried the children.

Miss Brown helped the children choose books.

And Jane helped a little boy find a good book about turtles.

FESTIVAL
Some Turtles

On the way home, they saw Joe in his sailboat.

He waved to them.

"Joe learned a lot from that book about sailing," said Jane.

"You will make a good librarian, someday," said Miss Brown. "I hope that you will come and work with me."

LIBRARY

34 2279